# Thomas Edison

By United Library

# Table of Contents

# Introduction

**Do you want to know the story of one of the most important inventors in American history?**

Thomas Edison is known as one of the most prolific inventors in American history. He developed and patented many devices that changed the way we live today. This biography tells his amazing story - from his early days as an inventor, to his work developing the light bulb and phonograph, to his later years as a scientist and businessman.

Thomas Edison was an American genius inventor and scientist who created some of the most revolutionary inventions in history. Known as the "Wizard of Menlo Park," he held a record 1,093 US patents in his name and was credited with inventing the first practical electric light bulb, phonograph, and motion picture camera. His inventions revolutionized the way people lived and changed the world forever.

He also contributed to advancements in electricity generation and distribution, mining technologies, chemical engineering, telegraphy, sound recording, communication devices, and electrical motors. At age 10 he started work as a newsboy on a train to help his struggling family make ends meet but went on to become one of the greatest innovators of all time in fields from technology to business. His impact on modern life is undeniable.

Edison's life is a true rags-to-riches story, and this book chronicles it all. If you're interested in invention, business, or just want to read a great biography, then this book is for you.

# Thomas Edison

**Thomas Alva Edison** (born February 11, 1847 in Milan, Ohio; † October 18, 1931 in West Orange, New Jersey) was a U.S. inventor, electrical engineer, and entrepreneur specializing in electricity and electrical engineering. His merits are based primarily on the marketability of his inventions, which he was able to combine into a system of power generation, power distribution, and innovative consumer electrical products. Edison's fundamental inventions and developments in the fields of electric light, telecommunications, and media for sound and image had a major impact on general technical and cultural development. In later years, he achieved important developments in process engineering for the chemical and cement fields. His organization of industrial research shaped the development work of later companies.

Edison's achievements in the electrification of New York and the introduction of electric light mark the beginning of the comprehensive electrification of the industrialized world. This epochal change is particularly associated with his name. His well-known developments include the phonograph.

# Life

**Youth and beginning of career as telegraph operator (1847 to 1868)**

Thomas Alva Edison was born on February 11, 1847, in Milan, a village in northern Ohio, the seventh child of Samuel Ogden Edison (1804-1896) and Nancy Matthews Elliott (1810-1871). His mother worked for a time as a teacher, and his father engaged in frequently changing self-employment activities, including gravel mining, farming, and land speculation. He was a free thinker and political activist who had to emigrate from Canada to the United States. The parental home is estimated to have been intellectually stimulating.

Thomas Edison received regular schooling for only a few months. After that, he continued to be taught by his mother. When he was seven years old, the family moved to Port Huron, Michigan. Four years later, in 1859, he got his first job selling candy and newspapers on the Grand Trunk Railroad between Port Huron and Detroit. He used the train's long stops in Detroit until the return trip to read books in the library there.

Edison had hearing problems as a child and was hard of hearing all his life.

In 1862, he received instruction in telegraph techniques from a telegraph operator whose son he had saved from an accident. He then worked as a telegraph operator for James U. MacKenzie in Mount Clemens. For five years, from 1863 to 1868, he had frequently changing employment as a telegraph operator in Stratford, Indianapolis, Cincinnati, Memphis, Louisville, and Boston. During this time, he gained a profound understanding of telegraph technology beyond operation, as telegraphists were often required to maintain equipment and batteries as well. Working with corporate and newspaper telegraph operators, he realized the importance of this technology to many areas of business. He is said to have educated himself with electrical engineering books and journals at that time and began experimenting. In 1868, in Boston, he came into contact with the world of telegraph manufacturers, telegraph designers, and the financiers of this technology, and began developing telegraph technology himself.

## Rise as an inventor in the telegraph industry (1868 to 1876)

On April 11, 1868, the trade journal *The Telegrapher* published a report written by Edison himself. The subject was a variant of duplex technology he had developed for the simultaneous transmission of two messages over one line. This first publication by Edison also brought him to the attention of experts outside his personal circle. In 1868, he filed his first patent for an electric vote counter for assemblies. However, this was not used in Congress.

Members of Congress preferred the traditional slow method, as it allowed more opportunities to filibuster unpopular motions and to change other members' minds.

In 1869, Edison went to New York. There he met Franklin Leonard Pope, came into contact with the *Gold & Stock Telegraph Company* through him and became responsible for the company's entire telegraph technology. Later, he became a partner in Pope, *Edison & Co, a company* founded by Pope. Together, the two acquired patents for telegraphs with printing devices. Such were needed, among other things, to transmit gold prices from the stock exchange to traders. Another printing telegraph developed by Edison and Pope was to be specially suited for operation by private individuals or small businesses without specialized personnel. Together with other partners, the *American Printing Telegraph Co.* was founded for this market segment. The joint company *Pope, Edison & Co.* was dissolved again at the end of 1870. The joint patents and also the successful business of the *American Printing Telegraph Co. were* bought by the *Gold & Stock Telegraph Co.* Partly as a result of the cooperation with Pope, who was in contact with many trade papers and electrical companies, the telegraph industry became increasingly aware of Edison's talent. Pope and Edison's developments were also relevant in the telegraph companies' battle for the lucrative financial information services market.

From the end of the collaboration until his death in 1895, Franklin Pope had an opinion of Thomas Edison that differed significantly from the public perception. In technical books and articles for trade journals, he relativized inventive achievements attributed to Edison. As a patent attorney or expert witness, he frequently represented plaintiffs against Edison companies.

In 1870, Edison's first own workshop for development and manufacturing was established in Newark, New Jersey. His partner in the manufacture of course telegraphs was the mechanic William Unger. For the expanding business, Edison established a new workshop with mechanic Joseph Thomas Murray in 1872 and paid off Unger. These workshops for making course telegraphs and telegraphs for private lines had about 50 employees and had a production of about 600 devices a year. They marked the beginning of Edison's activity as an inventor-entrepreneur.

Through numerous collaborations and exploitations of inventions in telegraph technology, Edison's financial situation improved in these years. While he was still living with the family of his then friend Pope in 1869, he was able to buy his first own house and start his own family as early as 1871. He married Mary Stilwell. In 1873, his first child Marion was born. Edison's financial situation remained unstable, however, because the high costs of his development work and his own manufacturing workshops were offset only by irregular income. He had to give up his house again in 1874 and temporarily move into an apartment.

The central problem of the telegraph companies at that time was the efficient use of the expensive telegraph lines. Automatic telegraphs, which rapidly transmitted messages prefabricated on paper punched strips, were conceived by Julius Wilhelm Gintl and developed to application maturity in England by Joseph Barker Stearns (1831-1895). However, they did not work on the long distances of telegraph lines in America. Edison was able to solve the problem of signal quality and further speed up the telegraphs. In particular, message recording at the receiver had to be further developed to meet the speed requirements. From 25 to 40 words per minute for the manual telegraphs and 60 to 120 words for the original invention of the automatic telegraph, Edison improved transmission speed to 500 to 1000 words per minute.

An attempt to sell the technology to the *British Post Office Telegraph Department failed*. During a trip to London in 1873, Edison noted in particular problems with his solution involving underground telegraph lines. The realization of knowing less than he thought he knew, as well as contact with more advanced electrical engineering in England, probably prompted the expansion of his development activities to include experimental research and more intensive study of technical literature.

With the *quadruplex telegraph,* Edison developed a technique for the simultaneous transmission of four messages and thus further increased the usefulness of telegraph lines. His solution was to use voltage amplitude to transmit one message (amplitude modulation) and polarity for the second message (phase modulation). He combined this technique with the well-known duplex technique, which allowed simultaneous transmission of messages in both directions. Telegraph companies that had rights to this technology saved large amounts of money on the otherwise necessary expansion of their transmission capacities through additional lines.

The sale of rights to the quadruplex technology and other inventions in early 1875 opened up new opportunities for Edison. He profited from the intention of railroad industrialist Jay Gould to build a network with the *Atlantic and Pacific Telegraph Co. that would* compete with the market leader *Western Union.* Gould was able to easily copy *Western Union*'s approach of building telegraph lines along railroad tracks, and he bought the rights to powerful technology from Edison. With the proceeds, Edison was able to rectify his then precarious financial situation and set up his first inventor's laboratory in Newark, which he expanded shortly afterwards and moved to Menlo Park. With Charles Batchelor, Charles Wurth and John Kruesi, employees from his telegraph manufacturing workshops, and the newly hired James

Adams, Edison made research, invention and development his core activity.

The development of the electric pen, which began in 1875, and a copying and printing technique based on it, which was later developed into mimeography, was inspired by work on telegraph technology. The invention was patented by U.S. Patent 180,857, dated August 8, 1876, as *Autographic Printing*. It was Edison's first attempt to generate regular income through inventions and their marketing. Using an Edison patent, inventor and entrepreneur Albert Blake Dick developed a version without electrics, sold the product as the *Edison Mimeograph* and achieved high sales figures for decades. By 1889, he had sold about 20,000 machines in the U.S. and established copying technology in businesses and government agencies. The devices produced by Edison himself were considered "too technical" and were far less successful. While the telegraphy inventions were about infrastructure for a few interested parties, the electric pen was Thomas Edison's first product for the mass market with the special importance of advertising, sales and customer reactions. His employees Adams and Batchelor shared in the proceeds.

Briefly, Edison was involved in a scientific dispute over an effect he discovered called *Etheric Force*, which later turned out to be the discovery of high-frequency electromagnetic waves. However, he failed to develop his advanced experiments on wireless telegraphy.

Thomas Edison had a contractual relationship with the important *Western Union Telegraph Co.* The company paid him for the development of acoustic telegraphy. In 1869 to 1875, he had established his reputation as an inventor in telegraph technology and had worked out the financial prerequisites for his further achievements. By 1875, Edison was a well-known man in the industry, reported on in trade journals. However, he did not become known to the general public until the following years. From then on, telegraph technology was no longer the focus of his work.

Franklin Pope, Marshall Lefferts, the president of the *Gold and Stock Telegraph Co.* , and William Orton, the president of the *Western Union Telegraph Co., are* regarded as key pioneers in Thomas Edison's further rise. He owes a network of relationships with newspapers, technology companies and patent attorneys to Pope in particular. Contacts with investors and knowledge of financing and the need for a business plan were owed to Lefferts and Orton, who also promoted Edison's reputation among other businessmen. From them, in particular, he learned that to take control of a technological venture, one needs a complete set of all the necessary patents.

## The Edison Laboratory in Menlo Park, Founding Years (1876 to 1880)

On July 18, 1877, Edison conceived the phonograph, which was developed over the following months. Unlike many of his other inventions, this one was something fundamentally new and not a further development of known technology. Edison's work on automatic telegraphs that sent text stored on embossed strips of paper led to the discovery that the embossed strips of paper produced vibrations and sounds in the mechanics of the telegraph as they were rapidly executed. This observation was further developed by Edison into the phonograph. According to Thomas Edison's recollections, the first recording made with a working phonograph was a verse *Mary had a little lamb*. He wrote that he was "seized" upon hearing his own voice. In November 1877, the phonograph was presented to the public and on February 19, 1878, he received the patent. At the suggestion of entrepreneur Julius Block, Edison sent a phonograph to Russian Emperor Alexander III as a personal gift.

Also in 1877, Thomas Edison achieved a decisive step forward in telephone technology with the development of his carbon semolina microphone. However, he was only granted the patent for this after a long dispute with Bell Labs, which had acquired a patent from Emil Berliner that was later declared invalid. In the telephones already offered by the Bell Telephone Company at that time, the energy for generating an electrical signal was obtained in the microphone itself from the sound picked up. However, signals generated in this way were too weak for transmission over longer distances without the electronic amplification that was not available until the 20th century. Bell's telephones could therefore previously only be used in local areas. Telegraph companies competing with Bell, who themselves also wanted to implement new business models based on the telephone invention, commissioned Edison to develop a solution to this problem. Edison's carbon semolina microphone no longer extracts the energy required for the electrical signal from sound, but instead takes it from an external energy source. A suitably strong current fed in from outside is passed through the microphone. The sound waves influence the electrical resistance of the carbon grit filling contained in the microphone. In this way, a strong signal current is modulated by a weak sound pressure. Intelligible telephone voice transmission was thus possible over much longer distances. The economic value for the emerging telephone companies was considerable.

The use of the call *hello* on the telephone goes back to Thomas Edison, while Alexander Graham Bell preferred *ahoy*.

Edison realized that a proliferation of electrical consumer products required electrical power grids. Electric light was seen as a key product for financing them and for the willingness of homeowners to lay cables. The model was the gas industry's business model of central supply, gas meters, and the one-time sale of lights on the one hand, but the permanent income from regular energy deliveries on the other. In order to realize his vision of the electrification of cities, Edison and his staff worked intensively on all the necessary components, especially the incandescent lamp, switches and the electricity meter. A particular challenge was the design of suitable generators. The dynamos Edison initially built only for his own use could supply electricity for only 60 incandescent lamps. All components of the power supply infrastructure thus had to be redesigned and then manufactured in-house or by partner companies. A group of investors around J. P. Morgan provided $130,000 for the development work on the electrical inventions through participation in the *Edison Electric Light Co*. founded in 1878.

Previous inventors had also worked on the electric incandescent lamp. But none of them had succeeded in making it permanently functional and its energy consumption competitive with that of gas lamps. The advantages such as freedom from flickering and odor, lower heat emission and easier switching on and off could not be translated into practical products. Another unsolved problem was the division of light. Only a few lamps could be operated from a single power source using the solutions known at the time. Some physicists considered the problem unsolvable and electric light unsuitable in principle for replacing gas light.

Edison also initially failed with his attempts to improve the familiar incandescent lamps with platinum filaments. In 1879, however, he had his first successes with incandescent lamps using a high-resistance carbon filament and perfect vacuum sealing, with which he reportedly achieved about 40 hours of burn time. The breakthrough is usually associated with a test and demonstration on October 21, 1879; this date is therefore considered the invention date of the practical incandescent lamp. However, more recent source research cannot confirm this widespread account; laboratory records show that tests with cotton carbon filaments began on October 21, 1879, and that a lamp with a high-impedance carbon filament burned for about 14.5 hours on October 23, 1879. The improvement to up to 1000 hours of luminous duration took a further three years of development. However, presentation events in Menlo Park, especially on December 31, 1879, already impressed the newspapers and the public. This created public awareness of the dawning electric age. Edison was able to win supporters and tackle his project of electrifying New York. The basic patent for Thomas Edison's lamp development, No. 223,898 "Electric Lamp," was applied for on November 4, 1879, and granted on January 27, 1880.

The consumption meter, which was important for the business model of electricity networks, was based on an electrolytic measuring principle suitable only for direct current, and various other developments were discarded. The design was strongly influenced by Michael Faraday's experimental investigations of the electrochemical processes of electrolysis and his construction of the voltmeter. Edison's consumption meter was a further development of the copper voltmeter, later zinc was used. The core problem of the measuring range was solved by a parallel circuit which passes only a proportionally small part of the current through the meter; the patent was applied for on March 20, 1880. Edison compensated for the influence of temperature on the resistance behavior of the electrolyte with a negative temperature coefficient by using a coil resistor with a positive temperature coefficient. An incandescent lamp mounted in the meter housing switched on as a heat donor via a bimetal switch if the temperature dropped too much. Further developments were called Webermeters by Edison, in honor of the German physicist Wilhelm Eduard Weber. The development stage of the model exhibited at the Electricity Exhibition in Paris in 1881 was part of the development of the electricity industry worldwide in the 1880s as the Edison meter. Although the meter had a high degree of accuracy, was not very susceptible to malfunctions due to the elimination of mechanical parts, and had very low inherent consumption, consumers were often skeptical because consumption could not be read. To determine consumption, employees of the electricity industry had to remove the electrodes and weigh them out on a precision balance; one gram of weight difference corresponded to 1000 lamp burning hours. For safety, each meter had a second electrolytic measuring device designed for one gram of anode weight loss per 3000 lamp burning hours. One lamp burning hour corresponds to 800 mAh, or 88 Wh at 110 V Edison mains voltage.

After public demonstrations of the phonograph to the President of the United States and elsewhere in April 1878, the domestic and European press first celebrated Thomas Edison as a great inventor. He also impressed the public in December 1879 with previously unknown light demonstrations involving instantaneous switching on and off of a large number of incandescent lamps, and in 1880 with the installation of his lighting system on the newly built steamship SS *Columbia*. Beginning in the late 1870s, not only trade journals but also daily newspapers reported on Edison, making him a world-renowned figure. Some newspapers called him the "Wizard of Menlo Park." This term, coined by William Augustus Croffut, became an established concept in American culture.

**The Electrification of New York and the Establishment of an Electric Company (1881 to 1886)**

In the years that followed, the focus of Edison's personal work shifted away from development and toward the marketing and implementation of electrification projects. At times, he moved his residence and parts of his development team from Menlo Park to New York. Whereas until then production sites had mostly had the character of workshops, the manufacture of incandescent lamps and components for the mass business of light and electricity required the construction of factories and the development of rational manufacturing processes. Edison's first lamp factory, the *Edison Lamp Co.* , was located first in Menlo Park and then in Harrison, New Jersey. From its founding until April 1882, 132,000 incandescent lamps had already been produced there.

The *Edison Electric Light Co.* was founded as early as November 15, 1878. It had the right to exploit the patents developed in Menlo Park and in return financed the work of the development laboratory. The company founded subsidiaries and cooperative ventures in the USA and abroad and provided these and other partners with the necessary patent rights. This company can therefore be seen as the core of the electrical corporation that emerged from it. The *Edison Electric Light Company of Europe* was founded in December 1880, and in 1883 the *Deutsche Edison-Gesellschaft für angewandte Elektrizität (German Edison Company for Applied Electricity)*, later AEG, was formed through a cooperation with Emil Rathenau. By the end of 1886, the companies founded by

Edison were among the largest corporations of their time, with about 3,000 employees and about ten million dollars in capital. The individual Edison companies in the USA, however, had different ownership structures and interests. Edison's focus on licensing income from abroad rather than building a global company was not a sustainable strategy in particular.

Raising capital for the expansion of manufacturing capacity and for the large investments required in power plants and in the wiring of cities was the main problem until the mid-1880s. The lack of skilled workers for wiring and for operating power plants also stood in the way of rapid and safe implementation of electrification projects. Edison himself no longer had a number of key employees available in the U.S., as they had to attend to electrification projects and the establishment of companies in Europe.

For these reasons, electrification was initially carried by lighting systems with their own steam engine dynamo. For this purpose, Edison developed solutions for different quantities of lamps to be operated. Factories, for which gas lamps were a fire hazard, theaters, train stations and wealthy private individuals were the customers. For example, a theater in Boston was wired in a matter of days and over 600 incandescent lamps and a dynamo were installed. In 1882, the Mahen Theater in Brno was the first building in Europe to have an Edison lighting system installed. In Germany, the Café Bauer in Berlin in 1884 is considered to be the first building illuminated by incandescent lamps; the lamps were manufactured by Emil Rathenau according to Edison patents.

By 1881, underground cables were being laid in New York. Edison also invented electrical fuses, meters and improved steam engine dynamos. On September 4, 1882, *Pearl Street Station,* the first central power plant in the United States, opened on New York's Pearl Street; it was designed for direct current technology. In the office of banker J. P. Morgan, who had invested in the *Edison Electric Light Co,* the grid was started up by switching on lamps. The six steam engine dynamos constructed weighed 27 tons each and provided 100 kW of power, sufficient for about 1100 lamps. As early as October 1, 1882, 59 customers were supplied, and a year later, 513 customers were served. The *Edison Electric Illuminating Company of New York* (from 1901 *New York Edison Company*), founded in 1880 for the project, was the prototype for other local electrification companies. By 1911, the company operated 33 power plants, providing electricity for 4.6 million lamps used by 108,500 customers. This growth occurred analogously in other cities of the world and had to be managed technically and administratively. In Milan, Europe's first commercial Edison electricity network was put into operation in 1883.

The cost of power plants and grids had to be reduced for this concept to become widespread. The first electrification projects in smaller towns in the USA using alternative designs such as overhead cabling were ready for operation in 1883. However, finding suitable sites with sufficient customers in the vicinity of a power plant to be economically wired and financing these projects initially remained problematic. In order to utilize planned power plants throughout the day and operate them economically, Edison became involved with the development of motors and the electrification of rail vehicles. The process to investor acceptance of power plants and grids, and eventually to a self-sustaining wave of electrification, was slow. After successful projects, however, more and more cities without electricity grids were afraid of locational disadvantages and invested in power plants and grids; Edison was able to limit itself to the role of technology supplier.

The three-wire system of electrical power supply developed by Edison allowed smaller cross-sections of the cables and thus saved considerable amounts of copper. Edison thought in terms of systems and always kept an eye on economic factors such as copper prices, since the success of his project depended on the costs of gas lighting being undercut. In addition to the three-wire system, the invention of a special wiring technique was of great importance. It enabled constant voltage throughout the supply network (*Electric Distribution System*, patent

264642). Without this solution, the luminosity of incandescent lamps would have decreased with distance from the power plant.

The key product, the incandescent lamp, was continuously developed. In 1882 alone, 32 patents were registered in connection with incandescent lamps, their production and the manufacture of filaments. As early as February 13, 1880, while investigating the reason for the consumption of filaments, Edison had observed for the first time the incandescent electric effect, which was later initially called the Edison effect and is today usually called the Edison-Richardson effect after the mathematical description by Owen Willans Richardson. On November 15, 1883, Edison applied for patent 307,031 on an application of this effect. He used the effect to indicate voltage changes in a circuit and to regulate the voltage.

The years from 1880 to 1886, with activities in the U.S. and Europe and numerous company foundations on the one hand, but also technical problems and the need to react to them immediately as well as frequent lack of capital on the other, were very intense in Thomas Edison's life. Due to a lack of time, he had to leave decisions of great importance to employees, and he often did not have time for exchanges with his private secretary until well after midnight. The death of his wife Mary in August 1884 at the age of 29 coincided with this phase. His second marriage in 1886 and the final departure from his home and laboratory in Menlo Park marked the beginning of a new phase in his life.

After the death of his wife, Edison initially occupied himself with improving some of his earlier inventions. Among other things, he improved his telephone for the *Bell Telephone Co.* by using granules of anthracite coal for the microphone. This design remained in use until the 1970s. Furthermore, he found a solution to operate several telephones on one line. Edison collaborated with his friend Ezra Gilliland on this. In 1885, the two purchased neighboring properties in Fort Myers, Florida, and erected identical buildings. With his second wife, Thomas Edison regularly spent winter vacations there; later, the house became his second residence.

## Edison's laboratory in West Orange and the founding of General Electric (1887 to 1900)

In 1887, Edison moved the development work to a new laboratory in West Orange, New Jersey, about ten times the size of his previous one and the most modern of its time.

In response to the further development of *his* phonograph into the Graphophone, which for the first time used a wax phonograph cylinder and showed a considerable improvement in sound, by Alexander Graham Bell, his first cousin Chichester Alexander Bell and Charles Sumner Tainter, the three members of the *Volta Laboratory Association*, active in the Volta Laboratory of the same name, Edison for his part developed the phonograph further, after he had rejected an offer by the developers of the Graphophone to jointly promote the commercialization of their "novel" speech machines. By 1890, he had improved the phonograph *(Improved Phonograph)* and developed a *dictaphone* (*Edison Business* Phonograph, later marketed as *Ediphone*) as well as wax phonograph cylinders, whose recordings could be erased by scraping off the top layer of wax and the grooves engraved in it, and then reused. However, lack of time and money due to his intense involvement in the electrical industry caused him to sell the marketing rights to entrepreneur Jesse H. Lippincott, who then founded the North American Phonograph Company. An application of the phonograph in talking toy dolls, however, failed.

In the competition for market share in electrification, the late 1880s saw the so-called Electricity War between Thomas Edison and his competitors George Westinghouse and Nikola Tesla. Edison preferred the direct current system, Westinghouse and Tesla the electrification with alternating current. Edison's company conducted animal experiments with alternating current to demonstrate its danger compared to direct current. These later caused outrage among animal rights activists; at the time, however, the Society for the Prevention of Cruelty to Animals encouraged the development of electrocution as a painless alternative to the then-frequent drowning of stray animals. Animal experiments were also conducted by Harold P. Brown for the development of the electric chair, a commission from the U.S. government to Edison. Ultimately, Westinghouse's alternating current system prevailed in electrification because of technical advantages, and Thomas Edison had to admit that one of his biggest mistakes was to have stuck with direct current after inventing the transformer in 1881. Edison's solution with 110 volts DC could not be implemented economically in rural areas with long distances between consumers and the power plant, nor could the inexpensive energy from distant hydroelectric power plants be transported to consumers.

In 1892, the Westinghouse companies received an order to supply their AC voltage system and a large number of a newly developed incandescent lamp, the so-called *Westinghouse Stopper Lamp,* for the 1893 Chicago World's Fair. This was a particularly prestigious deal because the exposition celebrated the 400th anniversary of Columbus's discovery of America. The loss of this contract made 1892 a setback year in Edison's career. He also lost financial control of his electrical companies during this time.

Edison merged his companies into the *Edison General Electric Co.* by 1890 on the advice of manager Henry Villard, as the previous group of companies could no longer be managed efficiently. The merger of the numerous companies into the *Edison General Electric Co.* required a great deal of capital to buy out third party shares in the companies being merged, which came from investors including Deutsche Bank and *Siemens & Halske*. Edison did not have a controlling financial stock interest in *Edison General Electric Co.* He was a stockholder, had a seat on the board of directors, and was connected to the company through contracts as an outside inventor. However, several positions in the company were held by Edison's confidants; for example, his former private secretary Samuel Insull was vice president.

In 1892, this company merged with the *Thomson-Houston Electric Company to* form the *General Electric Co. This* was necessary for financial reasons, as bad decisions such as with alternating current, expiring patents, and high costs due to expansion and patent disputes put the company in a difficult position. The *Thomson-Houston Co.* brought into the merger the rights to alternating current patents that Edison lacked but needed to continue to participate in the market, as well as its experience with this technology. The head of *General Electric Co.* became

Charles A. Coffin, who until then had been head of *Thomson-Houston Co.* Elihu Thomson became the chief developer of the new company; his developments and patents led to successes of the *General Electric Co.* in the early years. Edison lost influence and importance. The merger was initiated by the other shareholders of *Edison General Electric Co.* and their analysis of the company's situation, especially the bank Drexel, Morgan & Co. In the mindset of the banks, including those behind *Thomson-Houston Co.* , reducing competition and cleaning up patent disputes through merger led to more reliable terms for investors. It is unclear when Edison was informed and whether he agreed or was forced. His close associates Samuel Insull and Alfred Tate reported that he was presented with a fait accompli and forbidden to use his popular name for the new company. Officially, Edison supported the merger, but with distancing statements such as that he had no more time for electrical engineering anyway. Electrical infrastructure and incandescent lamps played only a marginal role in Edison's further inventive activities. Edison's partner Charles Batchelor, who was a shareholder in the Edison companies and also became a shareholder in *General Electric*, worked in the management of *General Electric* until 1899.

As early as 1894 and 1895, Edison continuously sold General Electric stock and used the proceeds to finance his developments and investments in other industries. He also bought back rights he had previously sold in the phonograph business and the motion picture business in order to regain control over his related patents and their exploitation.

In 1891, the kinetograph, a precursor of the film camera, was invented in Edison's laboratory. From 1896, he worked on X-rays and the development of the fluoroscope with a calcium tungstate layer, which improved the image representation compared to Wilhelm Conrad Röntgen's solution. Edison's colleague Clarence Dally died as a result of the experiments, and he himself suffered damage to his stomach and eyes.

In 1895, together with chocolate producer Ludwig Stollwerck, a friend of his, and other shareholders, he founded the *Deutsche Edison Phonograph Gesellschaft,* based in Cologne.

Kinetograph, kinetoscope (playback device) and the world's first established film studio (the *Black Maria,* 1893) in West Orange made Edison the founder of the film industry. In 1893, he introduced 35-mm film with perforations for transport, which became an industry standard. In 1894, he made the film *"Chinese Opium Den."* A projection apparatus invented in 1897 made the film business one of his greatest financial successes. In Germany, Ludwig Stollwerck founded the *Deutsch-Oesterreichische Edison-Kinetoskop-Gesellschaft in* 1895 as Edison's partner in marketing the *kinetoscope.* The films produced in the early years simply mention the name Thomas Edison in the opening credits. However, this is to be understood as a brand name; Edison personally was hardly involved with film production. The entire development was probably inspired by Eadweard Muybridge and his invention of the zoopraxiscope. Technicians from Edison's film studio secretly made copies of the film The Voyage to the Moon.

An entry into the iron ore business, on the other hand, failed and became Edison's biggest failure. He had already developed a magnetic process for separating ore granules in the 1880s, tried marketing it in vain, and then invested in a few pilot plants himself with partners. In the 1890s, he then invested a lot of his money earned in the electrical industry and a great deal of his time in implementing the large-scale exploitation of ores with low iron content, but this never worked out economically. The investments in process development became as worthless as the purchased mining rights when iron ore deposits with higher iron content were discovered. In 1900, the process ran trouble-free for the first time for six months, but the ore could not be sold, and Edison ended operations at his mine in Ogden, New Jersey. Presumably, Edison had accepted a high risk because he wanted to compensate for the loss of influence over his electrical companies with an entrepreneurial success in another business field. Edison also sold his stake in the *New York*

*Edison Electric Illuminating Co. in* 1897 to finance the failed iron ore business.

The new business activities, with an association of about 30 companies and about 3,600 employees, were initially consolidated under the *National Phonograph Co.* founded in 1896. In 1911, the reorganization was completed and the company was renamed *Thomas A. Edison Incorporated*.

From the late 1890s, the *National Phonograph Co.* achieved high sales figures with a phonograph newly developed by Edison for home use. In particular, an inexpensive version with a spring drive instead of an electric motor sold well. Thus, 25 years after the original invention of the phonograph, the transformation into a mass-market consumer product took place. As the devices became more widespread, the demand for phonograms increased. For about 10 years, Edison remained the market leader in the segment in the USA. From about 5000 units in 1896, annual sales rose to 113,000 units and 7 million phonograms in 1904.

Although Edison invested most of his time and money in the development of capital goods for industrial customers such as electricity networks, telegraphy, telephones and iron ore extraction, the production of consumer goods for private consumers was his main source of income at the turn of the century. These new markets were just beginning to emerge as a result of increasing leisure time and rising affluence due to industrialization. In addition to the invention and production of devices, business models had to be found and distribution channels established for this purpose. Cost-efficient production and low prices were particularly important for the mass market. Edison worked intensively on automating the production of the phonograph and the duplication of sound carriers.

## Achievements and events from the turn of the century

Together with Ludwig Stollwerck, Edison developed the "talking chocolate" as a record with deep writing and a phonograph (optionally made of tin or wood) produced in 1903 especially for children that played music from such a chocolate record. This phonograph was called "Eureka", contained a wind-up watch movement made by Junghans and was sold in Europe and in the USA. Besides the chocolate records, there were also those made of durable material.

With the improved phonograph cylinders, in particular the less expensive copying process of the *cast gold cylinders* from 1902 and the longer playback time of the *Amberol cylinders* from 1908, Edison was able to withstand competition against the gramophone invented by Emil Berliner for a few more years. The main competitor in the USA was the Victor Talking Machine Company, which had well-known musicians such as Enrico Caruso under contract. Thomas Edison felt that the voices of well-known stage performers were not suitable for recording and produced well-known music with unknown performers who met his quality standards. Initially, only the brand name Thomas Alva Edison appeared on the recordings; the performers were to have as little share as possible in the business with recordings. To compete directly with Berliner's Schallplatte, Edison developed the Diamond Disc in 1911, a proprietary record format with depth writing, and the accompanying record phonograph. However, the shellac record market was expanding rapidly at the time; the supply grew enormously, especially in the lower price range. Despite technical advantages, Edison's invention failed to catch on due to higher costs and the limited product range. In addition, he produced unbreakable celluloid phonograph cylinders under the name *Blue Amberol Record* and the accompanying, very compact *Amberola phonograph.* By 1919, Edison had only a 7.2% market share in the U.S. for appliances and 11.3% for phonograms. Production of devices and phonograms for entertainment, including roller phonographs and sound rollers, ceased in 1929. After that, the phonograph with roller was marketed only as a dictating machine. A correction system for dictation machines was patented as early as 1913, and the Telescribe system (combination of telephone and phonograph) in 1914.

By 1910, Thomas Edison was involved in the construction of cement plants in Stewartsville, rotary kilns, the construction of prefabricated concrete houses and everyday objects made of concrete, such as furniture or a special phonograph. A rotary kiln he developed became an industry standard. His goal was to make cement production more economical by automating it, reducing energy consumption and sizing the daily production capacity to several times the usual capacity of cement production plants at the time. Overcoming the problems involved took years. By the 1920s, *Edison Portland Cement Co.* was the largest producer in the U.S. and generating profits. Edison improved the quality of the cement by grinding the raw material more finely.

In 1912, the Kinetophone was patented, a combination of film camera and phonograph (formerly sound film). Edison, along with other entrepreneurs, had founded the Motion Picture Patents Company in 1908 to control the American film market through the patent rights of the participating companies and the *General Film Company, a* distribution company founded in 1910. However, a court ruling under the provisions of the Sherman Antitrust Act declared the company illegal in 1916. Expiring own patents and the loss of income from the film business in Europe as a result of World War I led to high sales losses. While films by Edwin S. Porter in particular were still successful after 1900, production was no longer competitive later on. In 1918, Thomas Edison ended his entrepreneurial activities in the film business.

Thomas Alva Edison was friends with Henry Ford, who had started his career at the *Edison Illuminating Co.* and is said to have been encouraged by Edison to set up his own business in vehicle manufacturing. Edison's intensive involvement with the further development of battery technology can be traced back to the requirements in automobile manufacturing. The electrification of automobiles was hindered by inadequate battery technology. In particular, the familiar lead-acid batteries were too heavy. Railroads also had a need for rechargeable batteries. After preliminary work on the Edison-Lalande element and a long development period with many setbacks, the nickel-iron accumulator was perfected as a solution. The basic solution was found in 1904 and went into production. Customers were satisfied, but Edison was concerned about the failure rates. He stopped production and invested another 5 years of development work in detailed improvements. The *Edison Storage Battery Company* achieved $1 million in sales in its first year of production, documenting the market need. The numerous experiments conducted and carefully documented became an important data base for subsequent generations of battery developers. In the context of battery development, Thomas Edison designed cars and rail vehicles with electric drives. He saw such vehicles as the most important future market for accumulators and electrical energy from power plants. However, the development of internal combustion engines led to the displacement of electric cars offered by various manufacturers at the time. However, the disappearance of this market, which had initiated the development of the battery, was compensated by the diverse other demand. The battery replaced the phonograph and motion picture business as the foundation of Edison's enterprise. In particular, a compact battery developed in 1911 became the basis of safe electric lamps for miners, another successful Edison product. In Germany, the *Deutsche Edison Akkumulatoren Gesellschaft* was founded in 1904. The company merged into what is now Varta.

The USA purchased substances from the German chemical industry. With the outbreak of the First World War, supplies came to a standstill. This stimulated Edison's interest in process technologies in chemistry. In 1914, he built factories to synthesize phenol (carbolic acid) from benzene for record production. In 1915 he built factories to synthesize aniline and para-phenylenediamine in a few weeks, and in 1916 factories to synthesize benzidine base and the sulfate.

Together with other inventors and scientists, Edison made himself available to the government during World War I after the sinking of the RMS Lusitania by the German Imperial Navy to develop defensive measures against German submarines. He became chairman of the *Naval Consulting Board, which was* charged with reviewing proposals and inventions and turning them into prototypes.

From 1926, he retired from his companies. In 1927, his son Charles Edison became president of the umbrella company *Thomas A. Edison Inc.* On the occasion of his eightieth birthday in 1927, Thomas Edison was honored by visits from delegations from all over the world and by numerous awards.

In the last two decades of his life, Edison frequently had duties resulting from his celebrity. He was visited by well-known personalities, invited to opening ceremonies, and interviewed about current events.

The *Edison Botanic Research Company* was the last company founded by Edison in 1927. Harvey Firestone and Henry Ford were involved. The company was to seek national alternatives because of the USA's dependence on imports of natural rubber. The aging Edison once again became personally involved in this project with his proven working methods. A biological research laboratory was built in 1928 on the model of his successful *Menlo Park* development facility. Some 17,000 plants were tested, a process of extracting rubber from goldenrod was devised, and the project was turned over to the government. The process remained without significance as synthetic materials reduced dependence on natural rubber.

Thomas A. Edison died on October 18, 1931, at his home "Glenmont," Llewellyn Park in West Orange, New Jersey. U.S. President Herbert Hoover asked Americans to turn off the electric lamps, which were associated with Edison's name in the public perception like no other product, in honor of Edison on the occasion of his funeral. In the presence of Lou Hoover, Herbert Hoover's wife, as well as Henry Ford and Harvey Firestone, he was buried in Rosedale Cemetery in Orange, New Jersey, on October 21, 1931, the 52nd anniversary of what was then considered the invention date of the practical light bulb, October 21, 1879.

# Worldview, Politics, Culture

Edison was a political supporter of the Republican Party. Among others, he supported the Republican presidents Theodore Roosevelt, Warren G. Harding, Calvin Coolidge and Herbert Hoover. In 1912, he spoke out in favor of the introduction of voting rights for women in the USA. Edison had no schooling himself. He criticized the American education system and spoke disparagingly of the value of subjects such as Latin. He saw the training of practically capable engineers as his main task.

Edison personally decided on the musical pieces and performers offered on his recordings. However, he had an aversion to jazz music. Hearing impaired since his youth, he is also said to have selected performers based on the intelligibility of sung lyrics. Over time, the selection guided by his personal preferences rather than market demand developed into an economic disadvantage for his companies.

He advocated a philosophy of non-violence. On April 4, 1878, he joined the Theosophical Society. However, although he was an opponent of the death penalty, his company took on a government contract to develop the electric chair. Edison repeatedly emphasized that he had never been involved in the invention of weapons.

Thomas Edison criticized Christian religious ideas and campaigned against religious instruction in schools. He is quoted by newspapers as saying "Religion is all bunk ... All bibles are man-made." (All religion is bunk ... All bibles are man-made.) In October 1910, remarks by him in the U.S. attracted attention in which he rejected notions of the existence of a soul and its immortality. His second wife, a devout Methodist, tried in vain to change his attitude; he remained a religiously unaffiliated freethinker.

Paul Israel, who is involved in researching sources on Edison, points out that the latter's view of Jews was nuanced and there is no evidence of agreement with the anti-Semitic publications of his friend Henry Ford. Edison saw societal conflicts as a result of centuries of persecution of Jews and assumed that these problems would dissipate on their own over time as Jews were not persecuted further in America. However, Edison shared widespread prejudices about Jews, such as that they had a supernatural business sense.

# Family

Thomas Alva Edison's parents were Samuel Ogden Edison, Jr. (1804-1896) and Nancy Matthews Elliott (1810-1871). In his first marriage he was married to Mary Stilwell (1855-1884) from 1871 until her early death. The marriage produced three children, Marion Estelle Edison (1873-1965) (nicknamed "Dot"), Thomas Alva Edison Jr. (1876-1935) (nicknamed "Dash"), and William Leslie Edison (1878-1937). In his second marriage, Thomas Alva Edison was married to Mina Miller (1865-1947) from 1886 until his death in 1931. This marriage also produced three children: Madeleine Edison (1888-1979), Charles Edison (1890-1969) and Theodore Miller Edison (1898-1992).

Best known to the public was Thomas Edison's son Charles Edison, a Democratic Party politician who was for a time governor of New Jersey as well as U.S. Secretary of the Navy. His daughter Marion was married to German Lieutenant Oscar Oeser and lived in Germany from 1895 to 1925.

# Invention and development

Edison filed a total of 1093 patents in the course of his life and also filed others together with other researchers. In 1882 alone, he submitted almost 70 new inventions to the patent office.

*Mode of operation*

The laboratory operated by Edison in Menlo Park is generally regarded as the forerunner and model for the emerging industrial research and development departments of technology companies.

The search for a suitable material to make carbon filaments is an example of Edison's working methods. His employees found that fibers from fast-growing tropical plants would be well suited. Edison then financed an expedition to collect such plants. Extensive testing was conducted to determine the properties of the plant fibers, and after 18 months, the species of bamboo native to Japan, *Phyllostachys bambusoides, known locally as* "madake," was determined to be the most suitable. Patent 251,540 is dated December 27, 1881.

The records of the experiments carried out at that time for the development of the incandescent lamp and the electrotechnical infrastructure are said to comprise

40,000 pages. The empirical development of sought-after solutions in extensive series of experiments, combined with the understanding that every failure also brings the solution closer, is regarded as an important reason for Thomas Edison's inventive successes.

One empirical paper examined the relationship between Edison's creative productivity and the number of projects he worked on. In particular, the study found a positive correlation between the number of projects and Edison's inventive productivity over the same period. This positive correlation strengthened when Edison's age was considered as another variable. By working simultaneously on projects on different subjects, Edison always had the opportunity to channel his efforts as soon as he encountered temporary obstacles, especially during long periods of trial and error followed only by several failures in a row.

The ability to find and involve competent collaborators for upcoming problems is another reason. For many years, his most important partner was the Englishman Charles Batchelor, who was regarded as particularly skilled in conducting experiments. His special position among the employees is made clear by his 10% share of the proceeds from all inventions. The precision mechanic John Kruesi worked for Edison from 1872 and was involved in the implementation of numerous design drawings and sketches. Ludwig Karl Böhm, a glassblower from Lauscha, who had previously worked in Germany with Heinrich Geißler, the inventor of the vacuum pump, was the first specialist in this field on his team. Technician and organizer Sigmund Bergmann, mathematician and physicist Francis Robbins Upton, chemist Otto Moses, and electrical engineer Harry Ward Leonard are other examples of incorporating expertise to further Edison's business goals. Inventors such as Lewis Howard Latimer, who had already acquired his own patents in the field of incandescent lamp development, also worked for Edison companies. Edison, on the other hand, did not recognize the talent of Nikola Tesla. The latter left in a dispute and became an important employee of his competitor Westinghouse Electric. Tesla later criticized what he saw as Edison's unscientific way of working as inefficient.

The inventions in Menlo Park and later in West Orange were patented under Thomas Edison's name, but for the most part developed by a team of craftsmen, engineers and scientists under his direction. The kinetoscope and kinetograph, for example, are considered inventions of William K. L. Dickson, who worked in the Edison laboratory. The shares of individual team members in creative achievements cannot be precisely determined. In traditional public communication, the image of Thomas Edison as the sole intellectual author of the inventions was inaccurately created. Technological leadership, organization and financing were the focal points of his invention-related achievements from 1875 onward.

Edison is described as a charismatic personality. Menlo Park employees later said he made them feel like partners rather than employees. With relatively low pay, Edison offered his employees the prospect of shares in companies to be founded later, commensurate with their performance. When the development of the light bulb and the electrical infrastructure began to bear fruit, even the smallest shares held by his employees were worth the equivalent of several years' salary. The combination of a charismatic person with natural authority, team spirit and the financial participation of the employees were decisive for their high willingness to perform and the success that ensued. Edison himself supervised the few regulations, such as the recording of all experiments carried out in the laboratory books.

This form of organization and cooperation, which was successful in the development sector and tailored to the person of Edison, proved largely unsuitable for the emerging company with several thousand employees. It was not until the various Edison companies founded in the 1880s were combined to form *Edison General Electric Co. in* 1890 and *General Electric was founded in* 1892 that the deficits in organization, reporting and management were eliminated. However, this cost Edison a serious loss of influence over companies he had founded. These were temporarily without management in the 1880s because Edison was absorbed in technical problems and did not care about mail and necessary decisions.

Another feature of Edison's inventive activity is the buying up of patents, which, supplemented by further developments, were incorporated into new patents.

The invention process he established is sometimes referred to as the "invention of invention" and *Menlo Park* itself is described as an important invention. Bringing together scientific experimentation facilities with workshop facilities of various trades, assembling a team with a broad coverage of knowledge and craft skills, and organizing working conditions that foster creativity among all employees are now considered not only the reasons for Thomas Edison's success, but also seminal for 20th century technology companies. *Menlo Park* was copied by many industrial companies and was in particular the model for Bell Laboratories.

Thomas Edison commented on his concept for success with the words:

He commented without self-doubt on his style of management, which worked under the conditions of daily face-to-face communication in the laboratory, but was a likely cause of problems for his corporate alliance:

*Selected inventions*

- 1868: Electric vote counter for meetings

- 1869: Stock price indicator, print telegraph *(stock ticker)*

- 1874: Quadruplex transmission technology for telegraphy

- 1876: Electric pen

- 1877: Phonograph

- 1877: Coal grain microphone (for telephone)

- 1879: Carbon filament light bulb, incandescent lamp

- 1880: Magnetic metal separator

- 1881: Edison thread (screw socket for incandescent lamps)

- 1881: Electricity meter

- 1882: Electric power distribution system (single-phase three-wire network)

- 1883: Application of the Edison effect to a device for voltage indication and regulation.

- 1888: Electric chair

- 1888: Phonograph roller with deep writing

- 1891: Kinetograph

- 1891: Kinetoscope

- 1897: Projection kinetoscope

- 1900: Rechargeable galvanic cell

- 1902: Phonograph Roll *(Gold Moulded Record)*

- 1903: Rotary kiln for cement production

- 1911: Diamond Disc (record format)

- 1914: Nickel-iron accumulator

(Calendar year of the first patent application in each case. Further patent applications for improvements to the original invention often take place over many years. Invention, patent application, patent grant and start of marketing can fall in different calendar years. This is the reason for different dates in publications. The U.S. patent system at that time also provided for the registration of reservations on inventions in process. For example, a reservation was registered for the patent on the kinetograph in 1891, and it was granted in 1897).

One of Edison's inventions is still present in every private household today: the so-called Edison thread, with which incandescent lamps or compact fluorescent lamps ("energy-saving lamps") and, as the latest development, LED lamps can be screwed into the corresponding socket (hence the *E* in the generally known designations, such as *E 14*, *E 27*, etc.). The thread, which used to be made of brass sheet, but is nowadays mostly made of plastic, is characterized by simple production as well as safe handling even for laymen. The solution is said to go back to an idea of Thomas Alva Edison in 1881, which he then developed together with Sigmund Bergmann in his *Bergmann and Company's Shop in* New York. It was first patented on December 27, 1881, in patent 251554, and the lamp base was produced by a joint company. Bergmann sold his shares to Edison in 1889 and returned to Berlin. The solution continues to be widely used in successor products to the incandescent lamp and for other illuminants.

Edison did not always develop his inventions into products. He held a basic patent for wireless telegraphy, Patent 465,971 "Means for the Transmission of Electrical Signals," applied for in 1885 and issued in 1891. In 1903, he sold it to his friend Guglielmo Marconi, who was thus able to protect his own patents against copyright claims by previous inventors.

The tasimeter for fine thermometric observations is an example of an unpatented invention by Edison. Publication without a patent application means a transfer to the general public for use without copyright remuneration.

Thomas Edison's unsuccessful inventions include some seemingly bizarre ideas such as making furniture and pianos out of concrete. The patented preservation of fruit in evacuated glass containers, derived from the manufacture of light bulbs, was also unsuccessful at the time.

# Implementation in innovations

*Social transformation using the example of electrical inventions*

The technical solution and the potential benefit of an invention are not sufficient for a successful innovation process. Transforming a technical achievement into a social process that leads to a positive evaluation by consumers, investors and politicians is a difficulty that innovations often fail to overcome. Successfully overcoming these problems is an essential part of Thomas Edison's overall achievement in introducing electric light.

Edison, like other inventors and scientists, faced communication problems with innovations, as many of the terms associated with the innovations, such as dynamo, fuse, direct current or incandescent lamp, were unknown to large sections of the population, and most also had no idea about the nature of electricity. In addition to consumer acceptance, he needed the confidence of investors and politicians. The latter could have delayed New York's electrification for years with safety concerns about laying underground electricity cables. Finally, resistance from the gas industry and its lobbying of politicians had to be overcome.

He solved the task through personal contacts with decision-makers and the press, among other things, using his charismatic personality, self-confidence, rhetorical skills and popularity to achieve his goals. In contrast to the development work in *Menlo Park,* Edison had to communicate with a large number of actors for the implementation of his electrification project, present his plan in the conceptual worlds of investors, building authorities, etc., and ensure the cooperation of all actors.

He countered the problem of the lack of comprehensibility of the innovations through non-verbal communication such as show events with lighting effects. The company founded in New York was not called the "Electricity Company" but the "*Illuminating* Company" *(Edison Illuminating Co.).* The power plant was called a "light plant," and Edison used it to communicate that they were supplying light, not electricity; linguistically, he was building on what people knew. Since consumers would have distrusted a physical unit for electrical energy such as *ampere-hour* as a basis for billing, a conversion to lamp burning hours was made; Edison introduced the unit Lh (about 0.8 Ah) for this purpose. Great importance was attached to the design of lamps so that, in keeping with the taste of the time, they were perceived from the outset as beautiful and enhancing the personal environment. The design of the bulb itself as a bulb with a screw thread is still considered aesthetically successful. The light bulb became an iconographic symbol of "idea," "enlightenment," etc. Theater operators were particularly receptive to the innovation. As a result, electric light became present at focal points of public life at an early stage and was perceived in connection with culture and entertainment.

The integration of the innovation into an existing cultural system of concepts, meanings and values was essential to its success. As a result, the transformation of this invention into an everyday commodity at the various levels of society was particularly successful. Charles Bazerman, a university lecturer from the USA, analyzes aspects of this in his book *The Languages of Edison's Light*.

*Patent litigation - a side effect of successful innovations*

Thomas Edison made more than 2000 inventions, 1093 of which he patented in the USA. By October 1910, 1239 patents had been filed abroad, 130 of them in Germany. The inventions relate not only to innovative consumer products, but also to machines and processes for their production, process engineering, capital goods and other areas.

Edison mostly sold the rights of commercial exploitation of his patents to companies he owned or in which he was a partner, such as the Edison *Electric Light Co.* The *Edison Electric Light Co.* then in turn resold limited rights to electrification companies, manufacturers, or foreign patent exploiters.

The volume of patents developed by Edison made it increasingly difficult for competitors in the electrical market to develop products not affected by them in the 1880s. The rapid technological changes and the high economic value of the inventions as a result of the successful innovation process led to widespread disregard for the patents. This forced the respective beneficial owners of the patents granted to Edison to spend large sums of money on the legal defense of their property. At times, Edison's companies were financially unable to do so. The pressure to enforce the exclusive rights of use sold to third parties weighed particularly heavily on the *Edison Electric Light Co.* and the person of Thomas Edison.

Financially strong companies in particular were able to afford years of court battles through all instances and to continue infringing the patents in the pending proceedings. The benefits of participating in the market obviously exceeded the legal costs incurred. Furthermore, the patent infringers were able to use the duration of the proceedings to develop circumvention techniques. According to Edison biographers Dyer and Martin, there were between 80 and 90 lawsuits in the U.S. alone over the incandescent lamp patents, and at least another 125 patent lawsuits over the inventions related to the incandescent lamp in the electrical engineering infrastructure. In 1889, Edison had to establish a separate division to manage and administer the proceedings.

To date, no patent litigation is known to have resulted in a court-ordered cancellation of a patent granted to Edison by the U.S. Patent and Trademark Office. The numerous challenges were a means of competing for market share. Edison attributed the necessary merger of his companies with *Thomson-Houston Co.* among other things to high costs for patent litigation and reduced earnings from patent infringements.

The patent case of the *Edison Electric Light Co.* against the *United States Electric Lighting Co.* lasted from 1885 to 1892 and is said to comprise about 6500 pages of files. It ended with the Edison incandescent lamp patents being confirmed in all court instances. The *United States Electric Lighting Co.* was able to continue manufacturing continuously because by the end of the trial they had developed a new incandescent lamp that did not infringe any Edison patent. The United States *Electric Lighting Co.* got into financial difficulties in the meantime, but could continue to afford the legal dispute and expensive new developments, since the railroad industrialist George Westinghouse bought the company in 1888. The disputes between Thomas Alva Edison and George Westinghouse had a cause here.

In proceedings brought by the *Edison Electric Light Co.* against the *Beacon Vacuum Pump and Electric Co.,* the

*Electric Manufacturing Co.* and the *Columbia Incandescent Lamp Co. it* was claimed that Heinrich Goebel, a native of Germany, had invented the incandescent lamp before Thomas Edison, see the section there on patent litigation with "Goebel-Defense."

# Aftermath

*Summary of innovation impacts*

Robert Rosenberg and Paul Israel believe that Thomas Edison did not invent the modern world, but that he was involved in its creation. The Edison biographer Robert Conot describes Edison's achievement with the phrase that he pushed open the door.

The consequences of Edison's innovations in this sense have an extraordinary dimension. Global and temporally lasting changes took place through electrification and media for sound and image. New industries emerged worldwide. The perception of the world changed through moving pictures; with cinemas, new cultural centers emerged in cities. Electric light changed social life, which shifted to the evening hours; shift work also increased as a result of better light. Electricity networks made it possible to rationalize manufacturing processes and led to greater prosperity. The carbon filament lamps developed by Edison were the first electrical products to be widely used in homes, paving the way for today's widespread electrification of the home. The rechargeable batteries he developed spawned another wave of electrification, particularly of automobiles, ships and railroads. Edison was involved in the global innovation of the telephone, which changed processes in commerce, for example, with inventions that were an industry standard until the introduction of digital telephony in the 1980s.

The enormous changes are made clear by an event at the time of Edison's death. U.S. President Herbert Hoover wanted to have the country's power plants shut down for a short time in honor of Edison. However, this was no longer possible by 1931.

*Cultural influence of inventions using the example of the phonograph*

While Thomas Edison initially saw the use of the phonograph in the office as its main application, the *Pacific Phonograph Co. had* great success in 1889 in San Francisco with a coin-operated phonograph for entertainment purposes. This business model spread rapidly throughout the United States. As early as 1890, there were said to be about 1500 such phonographs in pubs, restaurants, ice cream parlors, etc., where people consumed music on listening tubes in exchange for paying a fee. In Germany, carnies copied the business model and were able to amortize their investments in a short time and generate high profits due to the large number of visitors. While some of the operators initially had to produce their own rolls to suit their customers' musical tastes, a new industry for the production and marketing of phonograms emerged in parallel with the change in music consumption. The success of coin-operated phonographs led to the design and manufacture of inexpensive phonographs for the home; devices and phonograms were a mass business around 1900.

The phonograph made music available at any time and place, independent of concert events. Among other things, this resulted in increased influence among musicians and accelerated dissemination of some musical styles. The pubs with phonographs in the U.S., for example, increased the dissemination of music by African Americans, some of which had previously been known only in the local area of the respective recording artists' activities.

This effect quickly became a global phenomenon; music was produced specifically for the world market. Some authors therefore see the invention of the phonograph as the beginning of the cultural globalization of music. The cultural significance of the invention for music is judged to be comparable to the significance of the invention of printing for literature. Both inventions led to a new dimension of exchange and mutual influence between cultural circles.

*Success as a businessman, fortune*

Contemporaries such as Henry Ford (automobile manufacturing), Jason Gould (owner of railroad lines such as Union Pacific Railroad) or John D. Rockefeller (petroleum) appear in the usual lists of entrepreneurial billionaires, but not Thomas Edison. His attempt to gain a dominant market position with light bulbs and electrical infrastructure had failed. In companies founded in the 1880s, Edison was often merely a partner, even if they bore his name. Partners, employees, and investors built factories, organized electrification projects, and held company stock. These companies paid royalties for the use of Edison patents, which was a major source of income for Thomas Alva Edison. Most of the electrical companies founded in the 1880s merged into *General Electric*, where he was a shareholder without controlling the company (no source is available on his shareholding in *General Electric*). In contrast, his later company *Thomas Alva Edison Inc.* remained under family control during Thomas Edison's lifetime. Most patents had expired and many inventions were technically obsolete. W. Bernard Carlson, professor of technology at the *University of Virginia*, sees in particular a lack of understanding on Edison's part for the software side of the industries he founded, with the consequence that he had to abandon business areas such as sound recordings and films during his lifetime. With the early inventions for telegraphy, which he sold for a few thousand dollars each, others made high profits. Edison companies did not benefit from the sales and profit growth of other industries as a result of the electrical inventions, for example copper producers.

The biographers Dyer and Martin portray Edison as an ingenious solver of technical problems, but not as a great business strategist. They even note a carelessness and negligence on his part in business matters as well as a gullible trust in contractual partners. One consequence of this was that Edison did not earn a cent from the exploitation of his electrical patents in England and Germany. The biographer Paul Israel sees on the one hand a high interest of Thomas Edison in the development of technologies and the foundation of new industries, but on the other hand a disinterest in the day-to-day business of once founded companies and a mismanagement to be blamed on him in the necessary reaction of his companies to changing market conditions and technological change. As a result, his companies were only dominant in the market for a short time. Edison was therefore "moderately successful" as a businessman in Paul Israel's assessment.

The Great Depression, which began in 1929, coincided with the last years of Edison's life and probably reduced the value of his estate enormously at the time of his death.

*Influenced company founders and careers*

Some men who were temporary employees of Thomas Edison later became inventor-entrepreneurs themselves:

- Sigmund Bergmann (electricity, turbines, vehicle construction),
- Robert Bosch (electricity),

- Henry Ford (automotive engineering),

- Sigmund Schuckert (Electricity).

Many Edison laboratory employees have gone on to successful careers. Examples are:

- Francis Jehl. He was hired as a lab assistant in Menlo Park. Because of his skill, he became a close associate of Edison and later worked for decades in Europe on electrification projects.

- Samuel Insull. Thomas Edison's private secretary became president of the *Chicago Edison Co.* and the *Commonwealth Edison Co.* He was later responsible for unifying the electrical engineering infrastructure in North America.

- William Joseph Hammer.

# Honors (selection)

In recognition of Thomas Edison's achievements, the USA has celebrated National Inventor's Day on his birthday since 1983. A star has been dedicated to him on the Hollywood Walk of Fame. Numerous institutions and streets, including in Germany, have been named after him.

- 1889: Appointed Commander of the Legion of Honor by the French President

- 1904: In commemoration of the first electric light bulb 25 years earlier, a group of Edison's friends and associates issued the Edison Medal. Since 1908, it has been awarded annually by the American Institute of Electrical Engineers, and since 1963 by the Institute of Electrical and Electronics Engineers.

- 1909: Edison awarded the gold medal of the Swedish Royal Academy of Sciences

- 1922: Edison receives honorary doctorate from Rutgers University

- 1927: Membership in the National Academy of Sciences

- 1928: Awarded the Congressional Gold Medal (highest civilian honor in the USA)

- 1929: Celebrations to mark the 50th anniversary of the invention of the practical incandescent lamp. Henry Ford had the Menlo Park laboratory reconstructed, and Thomas Edison, in the presence of U.S. President Herbert Hoover and well-known personalities, including Marie Curie, repeated the historic incandescent lamp demonstration of October 21, 1879. The event was broadcast by radio; special stamps and first-day covers bearing them helped make the event a national event in the United States. (In Germany, where Heinrich Goebel was believed at the time to be the inventor of the practical incandescent lamp, electrical industry associations responded with a celebration in his birthplace of Springe on September 14, 1929, a few weeks before the event in the U.S.).

- around 1931: Naming of the asteroid (742) Edisona after him.

- c. 1933: John Kunkel Small (1869-1938), curator of the herbarium of the New York Botanical Garden, named the plant genus *Edisonia* after him, which is now part of the genus *Matelea* (silk plant family). Thomas Edison was elected to the board of directors of the *New York Botanical Garden in* 1930.

- 1940: Film biographies *The Young Edison* starring Mickey Rooney and *The Great Edison* starring Spencer Tracy.

- 1961: Edison lunar crater named after him

- 1977: Presentation of the Grammy Trustees Award

In early November 1915, newspapers, including the *New York Times*, reported that the Nobel Prize in Physics was about to be awarded equally to Nikola Tesla and Thomas Edison, but in fact only Edison was nominated. In fact, the 1915 Nobel Prize in Physics was awarded to William Henry and William Lawrence Bragg.

# State of research

Historian Keith Near said in 1995 that of all famous people, Thomas Edison was the one about whom the least was known. What most people thought they knew about him was nothing more than fairy tales. Since the lifetime of Thomas Edison, accounts have been handed down, interspersed with legends invented by journalists to embellish their articles or by Thomas Edison and his associates for the purpose of self-promotion. Furthermore, an abundance of errors have entered the traditional representations.

A team of about ten historians has been working on the scientific processing of the extensive sources for more than 20 years in the project *The Thomas Edison Papers* at Rutgers University in New Jersey; there is no end in sight. Thomas Edison alone left 3500 notebooks with drawings documenting the creation of completed inventions, as well as sketches of unrealized ideas.

Publications from the period after 1990, which are directly or indirectly based on the source project, correspond to the state of research.

# Modern reception

Scientific source research in the history of technology and innovation research led to a changed view of Thomas Edison. The image of a heroic genius cultivated by himself and by the media was put into perspective, and the value of the achievements attributed to him shifted from inventions to working methods and the innovation process.

Regardless of the achievements, the person Thomas Edison is also judged critically. According to Edison biographer Neil Baldwin, he was a homo faber of the most extreme form, his intensive work was pathological, and his most sophisticated invention was his self-transformation into a cultural icon.

The term *Wizard of Menlo Park* has inspired many investigations. Joseph F. Buonanno, for example, cannot discover magic or unusual cognitive processes in his investigation. Rather, Edison had achieved extraordinary results with ordinary thinking.

# Germany at the time of National Socialism

At the time of National Socialism, Thomas Edison was sometimes portrayed in Germany as a super-rich American and ruler of *General Electric who* owed his wealth to stealing inventions from Germans. A sharp contrast was constructed by the propaganda between the selfish profit-seeking of unscrupulous Americans with the misrepresentation of Thomas Edison as a stereotype and Aryan ideal characters of the National Socialist ideology:

The propagation of a German light bulb inventor took place even before the time of National Socialism, starting in 1923, but initially without belittling Edison's achievements.

### Germany before the First World War

In the period before the First World War, technical innovations were also associated with Thomas Edison in Germany. In 1889 he took part in the meeting of natural scientists in Heidelberg and was accepted in the circle of academic scientists. Among others, he held talks with Heinrich Hertz and Hermann Helmholtz; both reported the meeting to relatives in letters. Werner von Siemens acknowledged Edison's epochal achievement in spreading electricity and pointed out that, in addition to the incandescent lamp and the power supply, Edison's development of a consumption meter was of decisive importance for the functioning of the business with electricity.

A survey conducted by the Berliner Illustrirte Zeitung at the turn of the century in 1899/1900 testifies to Edison's popularity in Germany at the time. The approximately 6,000 readers who took part voted Thomas Edison the greatest inventor.

# Other books by United Library

https://campsite.bio/unitedlibrary

CPSIA information can be obtained
at www.ICGtesting.com
Printed in the USA
BVHW092337290123
657302BV00015B/2414